The Litt
of Ma ...,
Problem-Solving

by Judith Dancer and Carole Skinner
Illustrations by Michael Evans

HARBORNE
PRIMARY
SCHOOL

LITTLE BOOKS WITH BIG IDEAS

Published 2013 by Featherstone Education, an imprint of Bloomsbury Publishing Plc
50 Bedford Square, London, WC1B 3DP
www.bloomsbury.com

ISBN 978-1-4729-0610-6

Text © Judith Dancer and Carole Skinner, 2013
Illustrations © Michael Evans, 2013
Cover photographs © Little Angels' Schoolhouse/Kirstine Beeley
Series editor: Sally Featherstone

Printed and bound in India by Replika Pvt. Ltd

1 3 5 7 9 10 8 6 4 2

This book is produced using paper that is made from wood grown in managed,
sustainable forests. It is natural, renewable and recyclable. The logging and
manufacturing process conform to the environmental regulations of the country
of origin.

**To see our full range of titles
visit www.bloomsbury.com**

Contents

Introduction

Mathematics is one of the four specific areas of learning identified in the EYFS 2012. It is one of the areas that is seen as key in indicating that children reach 'a good level of development' – children have to achieve the 'expected' level in both 'numbers' and 'shape, space and measures'. Alongside literacy, it is also an area that remains high on the agenda of leaders, managers and practitioners in schools and settings.

Maths is a subject many people lack confidence in; sometimes having struggled with it at school, they avoid, if possible, maths when grown up. If maths – and calculations particularly – seem intimidating for some adults, then problem solving in mathematics can cause even more anxiety. There is no 'safety net' of knowing the 'right answer' beforehand, and problem solving lends itself to investigation and exploration with lots of possible tangents. Understandably, this is the area of maths where many practitioners feel least confident and where young children, who are not fettered by 'right answers', feel the most excited.

This book offers solutions through adult-led experiences in which practitioners model problem-solving strategies, and also offers a myriad of creative ideas for developing enabling environments that give children opportunities to lead their own learning and to identify and solve their own mathematical problems.

The emphasis in this book is on using everyday objects and things that appeal to young children in the Early Years Foundation Stage – sorting socks, neckties and other clothes; playing with animals and cars; making and sharing food; block play; building dens; sifting for treasure; playing with water; and getting messy and moving around, indoors and outdoors.

Mathematics in the EYFS focuses on two things. Firstly, the content of maths learning – what children learn. Secondly, and equally important, recognising how children learn – that is, through playing and exploring, active involvement, and creating and thinking critically.
Effective maths learning involves children in thinking, doing and playing, indoors and outdoors, with adults as co-players and children as co-planners of learning. Maths in the EYFS is all about supporting children in making sense of their mathematical world.

The Characteristics of Effective Learning underpin children's development in its entirety, and are essential to problem solving in mathematics.

As the non-statutory Development Matters Guidance (DfE 2012) has identified, practitioners need to observe how a child is learning, noting how a child is:

▶ Finding out information and exploring

▶ Playing with what they know

▶ Being willing to 'have a go'

▶ Being involved and concentrating

▶ Keeping on trying

▶ Enjoying achieving what they set out to do

▶ Having their own ideas

▶ Making links

▶ Choosing ways to do things.

Creating and thinking critically involves children:

▶ Thinking of ideas

▶ Finding ways to solve problems

▶ Finding new ways to do things

▶ Making links and noticing patterns in their experience

▶ Making predictions

▶ Testing their ideas

▶ Developing ideas of grouping, sequences, and cause and effect

▶ Planning how to approach a task

▶ Making decisions about how to solve a problem and reach a goal

▶ Checking how well their activities are going

▶ Changing their strategy as needed

▶ Reviewing how well their approach worked.

All of the above will, at one time or another, be elements in a problem identifying and problem solving process – although, of course, not all at the same time and in the same problem. It is the development of these characteristics that practitioners will need to observe and support. Babies and very young children start out as curious, engaged and motivated explorers, investigators, problem-solvers and learners, and we need to ensure they remain so.

As adults, we are constantly interacting with numbers, space, shapes and measures in our everyday lives, but for a wide variety of reasons we may not see ourselves as mathematicians. As leaders, managers and practitioners working with the youngest children, we must nurture all children to become confident, capable problem-solvers and mathematicians for the future.

The role of the adult

Problem solving in mathematics for young children involves them understanding and using two kinds of maths:

1. Maths knowledge – learning and applying an aspect of maths such as counting, calculating or measuring.
2. Maths thinking skills – reasoning, predicting, talking the problem through, making connections, generalising, identifying patterns and finding solutions.

   The best maths problems for children are the ones that they identify themselves – they will be enthused, fascinated and more engaged in these 'real' problems. Children need opportunities to problem-solve together too. As they play, they will often find their own mathematical problems: how to make a piece of cord long enough to tie around a fabric den; how to fit all the blocks into a wooden crate; how to share out grapes fairly; how to carry all the toys from one location to another, and many, many more. One of the key roles of practitioners is to provide time, space and support for children – to develop situations in which children can refine their problem solving skills and apply their mathematical knowledge to the problems at hand.

Within a rich, enabling indoor and outdoor learning environment, effective practitioners can support the development of children's problem solving strategies through:

▶ Modelling maths talk and discussion: language, and talking through problems, is a vital part of maths learning. Children need to hear specific mathematical vocabulary in context. Practitioners can promote discussion through the use of comments, enabling statements and open-ended questions.

- ▶ Providing hands-on problem solving activities across all areas of the setting: children learn maths through all their experiences and need frequent opportunities to take part in creative and engaging experiences. Maths doesn't just happen in the 'maths learning zone'!

- ▶ Identifying potential maths learning indoors and outdoors: providing rich and diverse open-ended resources, which children can use in a number of different ways to support their own learning. It is important to include natural and everyday objects and items that have captured children's imagination, including those from popular culture.

- ▶ Devising interesting and relevant opportunities for working with numbers up to 20 and, where appropriate, beyond, in problem-solving situations: with a particular emphasis on understanding the relationships between the numbers up to ten.

- ▶ Supporting practical experience of using measuring skills and knowledge about shape and space to solve problems: everyday experiences involving length, weight, time and money.

How this book is organised

This book is divided into two main sections, which reflect the structure of the mathematics area of learning in the EYFS:

Section 1: Numbers

Section 2: Shape, space and measures

Each activity follows the same format and includes a range of ideas and possibilities as to what children could be learning, but is not prescriptive since flexibility is key in the early years and young children, by their very natures, are unpredictable.

Focus:

This initial section identifies possible areas of maths development and problem solving skills. As children will often be leading the learning, however, it is possible that they may go off on one of many tangents. For example, the adult may have identified that the 100 identical small bears provided offer lots of opportunities for calculating with numbers over 20, but one child may choose to line all the bears up and use them as a non-standard measure, perhaps even going on to make a bear tape-measure; another child may decide to fit as many bears as possible into a shoe box; another may use the bears to make a pattern. It is essential that children have access to open-ended resources and that practitioners not only remain flexible but also have the capacity to identify children's own maths learning.

What you could provide:

This section supports the government initiative for creative development, Enabling Environments. It lists resources you could provide to support the experience, but remember, these are only possibilities – you may have better ideas, or access to different resources. Most of the items listed are readily available in early years settings or can be sourced cheaply or for free. When you are making collections of items, e.g. socks, neck-ties, off-cuts of guttering, empty cartons or bottles, remember to ask colleagues, families and the wider community – it makes the task a lot easier!

Remember, when children are identifying and solving their own problems, they will often want to use resources you haven't identified, so make sure they have easy access to well-organised materials that are clearly labelled with words and photographs and are readily available at child height.

What you could do:

This section supports the government initiative for personal, social and emotional development, Positive Relationships. It offers suggestions about things practitioners can do to support children's problem solving: sometimes this will include modelling problem-solving strategies and offering alternatives, while on other occasions the practitioner's role is more about observing, listening, waiting and noting what children are doing and saying. If it is appropriate, adults can join in as co-players with children, helping them to identify or clarify problems. Practitioners should avoid taking over or monopolising children's play or offering 'instant solutions'.

In essence, sometimes activities are about problem solving together, and on other occasions the role of the adult is to provide time, space and resources and then observe, planning follow-up experiences to support the children's learning.

What you could say:

Also supporting Positive Relationships, this section includes specific vocabulary, comments and open-ended questions that could be included.

Talk is vital to mathematical learning – if children cannot talk about what they are doing and why in mathematics, it will be very difficult for them to move on in their maths thinking.

Children need opportunities to answer questions, but they also need opportunities to ask questions too, and practitioners need to provide scaffolding for children to develop and ask their own questions.

Remember to include specific vocabulary, open-ended questions and enabling comments in your planning. It may be helpful to laminate key questions and comments and specific vocabulary and display these indoors and outdoors, as prompts for practitioners.

Another great idea:

Of course, many follow-up and extension experiences will evolve from practitioners' observations of children involved in problem solving situations – what engaged the children? What enthused them? What are their current passions?

This section includes examples of other stimulating ideas, which could give children opportunities to consolidate their learning, or a tangent, which could provide a new 'hook' to explore and investigate.

Developing a Maths Learning Zone

All settings are different and practitioners are constantly planning to meet the needs of different groups of children. You could be developing an environment that caters for a small group of eight or less children in a room, or the Maths Learning Zone may be available to 120 reception-aged children.

It doesn't matter what the area of provision is called; it may be known as the 'maths workshop' or the 'maths reference area', but it is important that this area for storing maths resources does exist. Resources should be clearly labelled with words and pictures (clear or opaque storage containers are helpful) and must be accessible for children to make autonomous use of throughout the learning environment. In addition to the resources stored indoors and listed below, practitioners need to ensure a wide variety of resources are available outdoors to support children's maths learning. These will not be identical to those available indoors – they will often be bigger, noisier, messier and include 'more' of things, as well as using the physical natural and built environment.

You will need to make decisions about the amount of resources available in your individual setting, but you should consider:

Indoors

▶ Shells and pebbles, conkers, fir cones, twigs

▶ Wooden and plastic 2D and 3D shapes

▶ Pegs, buttons, beads, threading shapes

▶ Ribbons, decorative tape

- ▶ Ties, socks, gloves
- ▶ Keys, badges, buttons, keyrings, watches, clocks
- ▶ Sorting circles, coloured card and fabric squares, sorting trays
- ▶ Tins, jars, boxes, baskets, trays, bags
- ▶ Small world toys, animals, cars and people
- ▶ Cubes, blocks, bricks
- ▶ Standard and non-standard tape measures
- ▶ Timers, balances and scales
- ▶ Counters, dice, magic beans
- ▶ Number rhyme cards, CDs and props
- ▶ Number line and height chart
- ▶ Maths books
- ▶ Photos of numbers and shapes in the environment

Children also need access to a range of maths games:
- ▶ Puzzles – inset, shape, colour, number and floor puzzles
- ▶ Track games
- ▶ Lotto, snap and domino games
- ▶ Board and card games

Outdoors
- ▶ Wooden blocks, crates and tyres
- ▶ Guttering, plastic pipes, cardboard tubes
- ▶ Watering cans, water channels, buckets, jugs, funnels and tubing
- ▶ Cardboard boxes
- ▶ Rugs, blankets, lengths of fabric, pegs and clips
- ▶ A-frames, planks and barrels
- ▶ Wooden pallets
- ▶ Tree trunk sections
- ▶ Collections of natural objects: rocks, boulders, cones, shells, branches
- ▶ Sand, water, gravel and pebbles
- ▶ Shovels, spades, buckets, molds, brooms, sieves, trowels and forks
- ▶ Bowls, saucepans, jugs and ladles
- ▶ Growing area with gardening tools, access to water and a hose

- ▶ Chalks, paints and decorators' brushes
- ▶ Bats, balls, skittles, targets, bean bags, quoits and hoops
- ▶ Washing line at child height
- ▶ Number-line and height chart
- ▶ Resources to tally and keep score

Resources in other areas of continuous provision

In addition to the resources stored in the Maths Learning Zone, here are some examples of specific resources that may promote problem solving in certain areas of provision:

Water play

- ▶ Assorted plastic bottles, including squeezy bottles
- ▶ Assorted plastic and foil trays
- ▶ Jugs and funnels
- ▶ Tubing, guttering and pipes
- ▶ Nets
- ▶ Tea set and kettle
- ▶ Boats, people, plastic water creatures and fish, other imaginative play resources
- ▶ Flannels, sponges and towels
- ▶ Plastic frogs and ducks to support number rhymes

Sand play

- ▶ Containers of different sizes and shapes
- ▶ Assorted gloves and socks
- ▶ Paper bags and spoons
- ▶ Molds, scoops, spoons
- ▶ Balances and scales
- ▶ Shovels, spades and forks
- ▶ Sieves and strainers
- ▶ Imaginative play equipment
- ▶ Tiny things
- ▶ Things to sift for: treasure, nuggets, jewels
- ▶ Pebbles, stones, twigs and shells
- ▶ Flower pots

Home corner

▶ Shoes and shoe boxes

▶ Handbags, shopping bags, purses, wallets and coins

▶ Assorted food boxes, cans, bottles (duplicates to match and sort)

▶ Real, hard vegetables

▶ Balance and scales

▶ Cooking and baking equipment

▶ Crockery and cutlery

▶ Timers

▶ Assorted patterned fabric strips and clothes

Construction area

▶ Visual images of buildings in the local and wider environment

▶ Images of doors, windows and repeating patterns on buildings

▶ Flip-book of laminated images of earlier constructions, with children's comments

▶ Large range of construction equipment including large hollow and solid blocks

▶ Reclaimed materials, including boxes, guttering, plastic pipes, fabric strips

▶ 2D silhouettes for 3D blocks

▶ Clipboards and markers to record constructions

Section 1: Numbers

Egg box explorations

Children love fitting things together! Give them lots of opportunities to explore this fascination by providing egg boxes and interesting objects.

Focus:

Matching, sorting, decision-making and finding ways to solve problems.

What you could provide:

▶ Egg boxes and egg trays with different numbers of compartments

▶ A collection of interesting objects that can be sorted in different ways and which fit into the boxes – include favourite things and natural objects

▶ Post-it note and markers

What you could do:

▶ Observe, wait and listen and then, if appropriate, act as a co-player with children, following their play themes.

▶ Note how children divide the objects – do they sort them using different criteria? Do they match them 'one to one'? What strategies do they use for adding and subtracting?

▶ Note the problems that children identify and the strategies they use to solve them. What happens if they are matching shells to sections and they run out of shells?

▶ Follow a pattern a child is making, using another tray – if they put one object into each section, do the same.

▶ Support children's mathematical mark-making if they choose to use the post-it notes and markers.

What you could say:

▶ Talk to the children about what they are doing and why.

▶ Make comments about what you can see: 'I see you have got one car in each of the compartments'.

▶ Make comments about what is happening: 'Wow, that tray is nearly full – you needed lots of shells!'

▶ Ask questions: 'Do you think there are enough fir cones to fill the whole egg box?'

▶ Provide scaffolding for children's own questions and support them as they answer each others' questions.

▶ Make links with home experiences: 'When I buy my eggs at the farm shop, they are in flat trays like this.'

Another great idea:

▶ Provide rollers, cutters, cake cases, candles and candle holders, together with sparkly play dough.

▶ Supply empty chocolate and biscuit boxes that contain inner dividers.

▶ Encourage the children to divide the play dough to make 'cakes', 'biscuits' and 'chocolates' of the same or different sizes, and note the strategies they use for counting and calculation.

▶ Support children's role play about birthdays, parties and sharing out food 'fairly'.

Sort it out!

Make the most of an everyday activity and build on children's interest in 'things that are different' and 'things that are the same'. Children can use their own criteria to sort and count the socks.

Focus:

Counting in ones or twos, developing ideas of grouping and changing strategies as needed.

What you could provide:

▶ An interesting collection of socks, including baby socks, bed socks and football socks of different sizes (clean!)

▶ A laundry basket

▶ A washing line and wooden pegs

▶ A bowl of soapy water and another bowl of rinsing water

What you could do:

▶ Introduce the basket of assorted socks and observe the children's reaction. Do they explore them and talk about them, or do they put them into pairs automatically?

▶ Support children as they explore and talk about the collection.

▶ If children want to wash the socks and they haven't already talked about pairs, introduce the idea.

▶ Observe how the children peg the socks on the line to dry. Do they count them singly, or do they count in twos?

▶ Do children explore aspects of pattern and size as well as numbers? Do they create repeating patterns on the washing line, e.g. two small, two big, two small, or two plain, two striped, two plain?

▶ Create your own repeating pattern on the line and observe the children's response.

What you could say:

▶ Talk to the children about the socks. Encourage children to choose two different socks they like, then ask: 'Can you tell me something that is the same about the socks?'; 'What else is the same?'

▶ When the children have discussed similarities, introduce the idea of differences: 'Now, can you tell me something that is different about the two socks?'

▶ Introduce and model the use of descriptive and comparative language.

▶ Model counting socks, either individually or in twos. Emphasise cardinality (counting two, four, six, eight) and then ask the question: 'how many socks do we have altogether?'. Note which children re-count, rather than stating 'eight' straight away.

Another great idea:

▶ Provide a selection of boots, shoes and slippers, assorted sizes of shoeboxes, price labels and markers.

▶ Support children's role play about shoe shops.

▶ Encourage talk and mathematical mark making about sizes and prices.

▶ Observe the ways in which the children sort and categorise the shoes, boots and slippers.

▶ Talk to children about their home experiences. Have they had their feet measured in a shoe shop?

▶ Can children make a foot-measuring machine? What do they need to make it? How will it work?

Hubble, bubble, toil and trouble

This experience fits in with children's fantasy play and will appeal particularly to those children who enjoy playing in mud kitchens! This is a great opportunity for children to explore numbers and try out new experiences in a non-threatening, open-ended play situation.

Focus:
Calculating, categorising, mark-making and making decisions about how to approach a task.

What you could provide:

▶ Lots of assorted containers filled with natural materials such as leaves, pebbles, gravel, conkers, twigs, shells, fir cones, mud, sand and some 'treasure' – sequins, gold nuggets, jewels and glitter

▶ Jugs of water, plastic bottles, large mixing bowls, cups, a 'cauldron', spoons and ladles

- Make sure cloaks and wizards hats are readily available from the dressing-up corner
- Laminate a few 'spells recipes', e.g. 'To make a flying spell: mix three smooth pebbles, two twigs, four conkers, a pinch of sparkle dust, and five cups of water.'
- Coloured paper, pens and glitter for children to write their own spell recipes, and a 'Spell Book' to stick these in

What you could do:

- Observe, wait and listen and then, if appropriate, join in as a co-player with children.
- Follow their play themes; if they are 'mixing potions', join in.
- Watch how children sort or categorise the objects.
- Note the problems children identify and the strategies they use to solve them. What happens if they need seven fir cones and they run out?
- Support children's mathematical mark-making if they choose to write a spell or potion recipe.
- Note which children use number words in their play, demonstrate knowledge of the order of numbers or show an interest in representing numbers.

What you could say:

- Make comments about what you can see.
- Ask questions: 'Do you think there is enough potion to fill all the bottles?'
- Provide scaffolding for children's own questions and support them as they answer each other's questions.
- Model reading numerals: read recipes for potions and spells out loud, focusing on the numbers – one feather, three shells...

Another great idea:

- Set up a 'Mud Kitchen' with the children.
- Add woks, assorted cooking pans, baking trays, metal and wooden utensils, jugs, mixing bowls, sieves, colanders, laminated cook books, natural materials, chef's hats, aprons, oven gloves, tea-towels, and an 'oven'.
- Ensure children have access to a water supply – an outdoor tap or a water butt.

Down on the farm

This activity could arise from a farm visit or a child's fascination with farm animals.

Focus:

Sorting, counting, addition and reasoning.

What you could provide:

▶ Adult and baby small world farm animals in different sizes, colours and breeds

▶ Squares of fabric, carpet or turf

▶ Small boxes and fences

▶ Plants, twigs, pebbles, moss

What you could do:

▶ Set up some 'fields' and 'paddocks' and a home (such as a 'barn' made from a small box) for some of the animals.

▶ Position the animals randomly in different locations on your mini farm.

▶ Talk to the children about their earlier experiences at farms and seeing farm animals.

▶ Observe the children as they sort the animals into groups and put them in separate fields, paddocks and homes.

▶ Note the strategies children use when counting and sorting the animals – who lines them up? Who counts random layouts? who sorts according to shared characteritics?

▶ Where appropriate, model counting in twos with the children – do any of the children match the animals in pairs?

What you could say:

▶ Talk to the children about what they are doing and why.

▶ Model the use of the language of calculating: 'If there are six pink pigs and three black and white pigs, how many pigs are there altogether?'

▶ Note which children subitise, rather than count, when you ask the question 'how many?' for a small number of animals (which children know how many there are without counting?).

▶ Challenge children's thinking: 'So you have put the cows in the largest field, but are there more cows than sheep?'; 'What happens if you put all the sheep and goats in the same field?'

Another great idea:

▶ Introduce the Farmyard Game (a game for two players).

▶ One child has a square of green felt or card (the field), and the other has a shallow box (the farmyard).

▶ Make a cardboard disc with the children: two spots on one side and one spot on the other.

▶ Place 10 (or 20) animals in a basket.

▶ The children take turn to flip the disc and take as many animals as indicated (one or two).

▶ On each turn, they predict how many animals are now in the field and the farmyard, then count together to confirm.

▶ Support the children as they make up their own rules for another farmyard game – how do they decide on the rules?

It's in the bag

Shopping is a favourite activity for many children. Wherever possible, before introducing this activity, take children on a shopping trip to buy the vegetables, ensuring they have opportunities to fill the shopping basket, pay in cash and carry the vegetables back to the setting. Although the emphasis of this activity is on counting, children are likely to talk about shape, size and weight too.

Focus:

Counting, one-to-one correspondence, order irrelevance and making predictions.

What you could provide:

▶ Assorted sizes and shapes of shopping baskets and bags: wicker, string, cloth, plastic, Hessian and children's shoppers

▶ Lots of hard vegetables: potatoes, swedes, carrots, turnips, marrows and cabbages, in vegetable racks and shallow baskets

▶ Coins and purses

I will need

What you could do:

▶ Set up the baskets and racks of vegetables.

▶ Give the children time and space to explore the vegetables and make comparisons.

▶ Support children as they count the vegetables.

▶ Note which children count in the correct order, and those who make omissions or repeat numbers.

▶ Note which children exhibit one-to-one correspondence – which children touch or point to each vegetable individually as they count and match a number to each one that is being counted.

▶ Model order irrelevance to children: place the vegetables in a random layout and show children that it doesn't matter where you start, whether you start at the top, bottom, middle, or edges, the result is the same as long as each item is counted once.

What you could say:

▶ Talk to the children about the vegetables, naming them, counting them and comparing sets.

▶ Ask questions such as: 'Are there more carrots than potatoes?'; 'Are there fewer swedes than turnips?'

▶ Discuss which is the best bag for the vegetables. Can the children predict how many of each vegetable will fit into each bag or basket? E.g. how many cabbages will fit into the small Hessian bag? How many turnips?

▶ Use the language of calculation: 'If there are five carrots in one bag and seven potatoes in another, how many vegetables altogether?'

Another great idea:

▶ Make vegetable soup with the children.

▶ Begin with a group writing activity to make a recipe. How many potatoes do children want to use? How many carrots? How many turnips and swedes? What else do they need to make soup (e.g. vegetable stock, seasoning)?

▶ Chop the vegetables into small pieces with the children, using child-safe knives such as Kiddicutters, and with careful adult supervision.

▶ Simmer the mixture until all the vegetables are soft (adult-only step).

▶ Taste and enjoy!

Box of beans

Many children love to fit things into boxes, bags and other containers. This experience gives them opportunities to follow their fascination and explore mathematical mark-making, too.

Focus:

Counting, predicting, recording and being willing to 'have a go'.

What you could provide:

▶ Magic beans: in your preparation beforehand, spread 500g of dried white butter beans on newspaper, outdoors, away from the children. Spray one side of the beans with non-toxic metallic spray paint – gold or silver is best

▶ Assorted small nesting boxes

▶ A shallow bamboo or wooden tray

▶ Post-it notes and markers

What you could do:

- Fill some of the boxes with the magic beans.
- Give the children opportunities to predict how many beans are in the box.
- Observe the strategies that children use to predict.
- Note which children choose to make marks to record how many beans are in the boxes.
- Next, ask the children to throw the beans in the air and count how many land shiny-side up.
- Support children as they make mathematical marks – drawings, symbols, tallies or numerals.
- Line the beans up, some shiny-side up and some plain-side up. Can the children create patterns or sequences?
- Note which children show an interest in number problems and apply their own methods to solving them.
- Introduce the game 'hide the bean' – put one bean in a box, and add two identical empty boxes. Move the three boxes around and see which children accurately predict which box the bean is in.

What you could say:

- Ask children to predict the number of beans in a box.
- Discuss with children why they think there are three, or four, or ten beans...
- Talk to the children about the marks they are making to record numbers – can they explain what they are doing and why?
- Ask: 'Can anyone think of another way to remember what's in the box?'
- Model calculation questions: 'If there are five beans in that box and three beans in this one, how many altogether?'

Another great idea:

- Introduce the game '100 beans'.
- Two players take turns to throw five beans each. They keep the beans that land shiny-side up and put the rest back in the bowl.
- The game keeps going until all the beans are gone.
- Can the children predict who has the most beans?
- What strategies do they use to check their predictions? For example, do they group the beans in 'tens' to calculate the total?
- Support the children as they make up their own games using the beans.

What a lot!' – car showroom

As an effective practitioner, you should try to tune into children's passions and current enthusiasms. So if you have a group of children, possibly boys, who spend prolonged periods playing with trucks and cars, give them opportunities to find out more about maths!

Focus:

Classifying, sorting, counting, adding, subtracting and being involved.

What you could provide:

▶ Some unfamiliar trucks and cars and some old favourites – ensure these include metal, plastic and wooden vehicles, which can be sorted in different ways

▶ Masking tape and scissors

▶ Sticky labels and markers

What you could do:

- ► Mark out one or two 'parking lots' on a table top or smooth floor, using masking tape.
- ► Line the vehicles up around the edge of the table or floor area.
- ► Encourage one child to select two vehicles that have something the same about them.
- ► When the other children have identified what is the same, e.g. size, materials, colour, lorries or racing cars, the child selects a 'parking lot' to put the vehicles in.
- ► Another child chooses two more vehicles that have something the same – do they belong in the same 'parking lot', or a different parking lot?
- ► What happens when a specific vehicle could belong in both lots? E.g. if it could belong in the set of red vehicles and also belongs in the set of fast cars.
- ► Support the children as they discuss the vehicles, make new 'parking lots' with masking tape, and creating labels for the groups, if they choose.
- ► Observe the strategies the children use.

What you could say:

- ► Ask children to explain what they are doing and why.
- ► Introduce and model the use of the vocabulary 'the same as' and 'different from'.
- ► Ask children about the sets: 'Are there more diggers or more fast cars?'
- ► Where appropriate, talk about the number of wheels on the vehicles: if one car has four wheels, how many wheels do two cars have? Or three?

Another great idea:

- ► Make car number plates with the children for all the wheeled toys outdoors. Do the children know the format of registration plates? Can you take photos of cars you can see in the local environment?
- ► Make labels for each vehicle and a car-parking bay for each – if you have eight toys with wheels, chalk out eight parking bays.
- ► Create 'Car Parking Attendant' caps and parking-ticket writing frameworks.
- ► Support children as they chalk roadways – perhaps adding bus stops, zebra crossings and other familiar features.

Domino select

Use the dominoes in your setting to encourage children's interest in number problems and to support their growing knowledge about number.

Focus:

Counting, addition, difference, explaining and making connections.

What you could provide:

▶ A large selection of dominoes (it doesn't matter if they are from different sets or that they are incomplete sets)

▶ Some large spotty dice

▶ A bag to put some of the dominoes in

What you could do:

▶ Make connections between different mathematical ideas by drawing attention to adding the number of spots together, or working out aloud the number difference between the two halves of a domino.

▶ Sort out the dominoes that are doubles and identify together which one has the most spots or the fewest spots.

▶ Put a few dominoes in a bag and ask a child to secretly remove a domino, count the spots, say the total and ask everyone to guess how many spots are on each half of the domino.

▶ Play a game of 'Spot the Domino'. Spread all the dominoes face up. Roll two large spotty dice, say the two numbers that you threw and ask the children to find a domino with the same numbers as the two dice.

▶ Challenge children to make a line of dominoes that has 20 spots altogether.

What you could say:

▶ Match together two dominoes that have the same number and observe out loud that you've put them together because they've got the same number of spots.

▶ Emphasise the fact that a double domino has double the number of spots on one side as it does on the other, but also that each side of the domino equals half of the total number of spots.

▶ Talk to children about not needing to count the spots on each side of the domino if they recognise the spot pattern.

▶ Ask questions such as: 'Can anyone find a domino that has five spots altogether?'

Another great idea:

▶ Use postcards, stickers and spots to make your own dominoes. You could attach them to a washing line of numbers to make a domino number line. Most numeral cards on the washing line will have more than one domino card attached to them. For instance, the number four might have two dominoes attached to it: a three-spot and one-spot domino, and a double two-spot domino.

▶ Reception-age children could be challenged to create a domino number line to 20 by using or making a double-nine spot set of dominoes as well. Note the children who are able to suggest ways of creating 19 and 20 on the domino line.

Mobile phone shop

Children are constantly observing adults answering mobile phones, texting, taking photos or downloading information, and are usually quite keen to get their hands on one!

Focus:

Recognising numerals, inventing number strings, solving a problem by being systematic.

What you could provide:

▶ A selection of redundant mobile phones (real and toy)
▶ Calculators
▶ Number lines
▶ Number cards
▶ Telephone directories
▶ A till with a credit card reader
▶ Luggage labels

What you could do:

▶ Make pretend phone calls and rehearse answering 'hello' and saying a number string.
▶ Discuss with the children who they would phone and what they would say to that person if they had their own mobile phone.

- ▶ Use phone directories to look up phone numbers and write them down. Do not phone these numbers!
- ▶ Encourage children to recall numbers that are personal to them, such as their age or door number.
- ▶ Suggest they use a calculator to record the numbers they are going to dial on their mobile phone.
- ▶ Choose some numbers and invent number sequences together.

What you could say:

- ▶ Support children in identifying numerals by identifying their positions on the number line, and by making statements such as: 'Look at the number line! Can you find a five? It's the number that comes between four and six.'
- ▶ Discuss with the children how they knew which numbers to press and how they remembered the sequence. Talk about how to solve the problem if they forget the sequence.
- ▶ Help children to focus on a numeral by making observations such as 'I wonder what a nine looks like?'
- ▶ Ask questions such as: 'Who could suggest what numbers we could try next?' or 'Where could we find the phone number you need to dial to contact the doctor?'
- ▶ When children are playing with a large calculator, ask what numbers they can make the calculator display.
- ▶ Make comments such as: 'I wonder if it would be a good idea to make a list of numbers to put up in the mobile phone shop?'

Another great idea:

- ▶ Set up a repair and workshop area as a space for investigating how things work.
- ▶ Resource the workshop with simple objects that can be taken apart and put together again, as well as machines that have push-button keypads and dials.
- ▶ Introduce a collection of redundant TV remote controls for children to examine. Focus on the numerals on the handsets.
- ▶ Suggest children use nuts and bolts, keys and recycled materials from the construction area to build their own machines. Provide dials and controls with numerals on to enhance fantasy play with the built machines.

Carrot cakes

This game is good for helping children to begin to focus on different combinations of numbers and to use the strategy of 'counting on' to solve number problems. It works best with groups of two or three.

Focus:

Counting, counting on, solving a problem through decision making.

What you could provide:

▶ A jam tart tin with a paper cupcake case in each indentation

▶ A one to three dice and a small dish containing raw carrots cut into slices

What you could do:

▶ Take it in turns to toss the dice, pick up the number of carrot slices indicated on the dice, and distribute them amongst the cake cases. Set the rule that each cake case is full when it has ten pieces of carrot in it.

▶ Involve children in making or adapting the rules in any dice games they are playing. Children could decide that all the pieces of carrot from one dice throw must be put in one cake case, or they could decide that the carrot pieces should be distributed amongst all the cake cases.

▶ Rehearse skills such as counting, and note any misconceptions or misunderstandings.

▶ Observe whether children are able to count an irregular arrangement of five or ten objects, and the methods they use to count on. They should be able to count how many additional carrots they put in the case each time without starting again from one.

▶ Note the strategies children use to establish how many carrots there are, and to count on.

What you could say:

▶ Encourage children to make decisions during the game – you can achieve this by making some 'either/or' statements.

▶ Model a counting-on strategy by counting aloud and counting on as you add more pieces of carrot to a cake case.

▶ Make statements such as: 'I wonder which case has the fewest pieces of carrot?'

▶ Ask challenging questions such as 'How many more carrot pieces does that cake case need in it to make ten?'

Another great idea:

▶ Bake an actual carrot cake with the children, cut into small slices and play the game again. Choose a new number for each cake case.

▶ Alternatively, use counters or plastic dinosaurs instead of carrots.

▶ Use ten large plastic container lids, counters and a one to six dice. Label each lid with a number from one to ten. Take it in turns to toss the dice and pick up that many counters. Distribute the counters among the lids. Keep playing until all the lids have the same number of counters as written on the lid label.

Banking

Choice is an important part of problem solving, as it leads onto decision making. In this activity, children handle real coins and in doing so it creates opportunities for them to examine coins and choose how to sort, count and stack them. It also supports children in beginning to understand that different coins have different values.

Focus:
Counting, sorting, using the vocabulary of money and decision making.

What you could provide:

▶ A collection of real coins, mostly 1p, 2p and 5p pieces. Soak the coins in a fizzy drink overnight to remove any discolouration

▶ Some small purses, money boxes, tins and plastic boxes

▶ Coin sorting trays and machines

What you could do:

▶ Play alongside the children, sorting and counting the coins into piles and putting them in purses.

▶ Look for coins that are the same and model putting them in piles of ten.

▶ Play a game of tossing coins and identifying whether they land on heads or tails.

▶ Look for numbers on the coins. Show how to identify how much each coin is worth by pointing out the numeral '1' on the 1p coin and the '2' on the 2p coin. Discuss the differences between a 1p coin and a 2p coin.

▶ Set up a bank or post office where children can pay in and take out money.

▶ Find out how many 1p coins it takes to cover the front cover of a book, or any other object).

▶ Make a list of things that you can buy for 10p or 20p or £1.

What you could say:

▶ Support children by encouraging discussions on how they sorted the coins. Make statements such as: 'I expect you thought you'd look for all the 1p coins first – or did you do something different?'

▶ Ask questions such as: 'Does anybody know the names of any coins we use?'

▶ Encourage children to describe how they are arranging and counting the coins they have sorted.

▶ Make links with using the coins to buy things.

Another great idea:

▶ Throw a spotty one to six dice and pick up as many coins as the number on the dice displays. Put the coins in a line; keep taking turns and adding to the line until it reaches across the table.

▶ Set up a 'pound and pence' stall in the outdoor area and charge £1 or 10p for every item (use plastic coins in this role-play). Provide the children with stickers and pens to price the items. Show the children a real one pound coin and a 10p, and encourage them to identify the differences in the look and feel of both coins.

Making number lines

Developing flexibility with mental calculation is much easier if children have an understanding of how to use a number line. This problem solving activity involves children working together to produce their own number lines using a range of materials.

Focus:

Putting numbers in order, using 'one more' and 'one less'; making decisions about how to approach a task, solve a problem and reach a goal.

What you could provide:

▶ Empty washing line and pegs

▶ Number cards from 1 - 10 or 1 - 20

▶ Glue and spreaders

▶ Craft materials such as beads, sequins and pom-poms

What you could do:

▶ Establish the purpose of a number line and how the children could use it.

▶ Explain that the setting needs a new number line and it would be helpful if they could make one for everyone to use.

▶ Look at your existing number lines and tracks and ask for suggestions as to how you can put together a new number line.

▶ If the children are not sure how to go about this, suggest children take a number card and stick the number of objects that matches the numeral onto the card.

▶ When the cards are all made, the children should peg them in the right order on the washing line.

What you could say:

▶ Model the act of counting along a number line so that you can find out where a particular number fits in.

▶ Ask questions such as: 'Has anybody made the number that is one more than six?'

▶ Deliberately put a number card in the wrong position and wonder aloud if it is in the right place.

▶ Make comments and suggestions on the number of objects there should be on a particular card: 'How did you know how many sequins to glue onto the number seven card?'

▶ Can you tell me where you think Aimee is going to put the number eight?'

Another great idea:

▶ Make an interactive number line. Write numerals on small beach buckets and suspend on a line at child-height in the outdoor area. Suggest children put the appropriate number of objects in each bucket.

▶ In the Autumn, make a collection of conkers, leaves and fir cones and support children in stringing together collections such as five leaves, six conkers, seven fir cones – and then suspend on a line across the outdoor area. Children may need help using a bradel to make the holes in the conkers, florists wire or raffia to wind round the top of a fir cone, and hole punch for making holes in the leaves.

Letter plates

This sorting and collecting game played with dice and small world toys usually gives children the time and inclination for lots of talk, as well as involving them in making choices as they play.

Focus:

Counting, calculating, making decisions.

What you could provide:

▶ Five small paper plates labelled 'a', 'b', 'c', 'd' and 'e'

▶ In a basket, five apples, five plastic bears, five crayons, five dinosaurs and five elephants – or alternative objects whose initial letters are 'a', 'b', 'c', 'd' and 'e'

▶ One soft toy

▶ A dice labelled 'a', 'b', 'c', 'd' and 'e', and the sixth face labelled with a question mark

What you could do:

▶ Support children in sorting the objects into sets of the same object, and help them to identify the title of each set as indicated by the letter.

- Draw children's attention to this relationship between the letter on the plate and the initial letter of each object. Show the dice and explain about the letters on the dice and the question mark, which means 'you can choose the letter!'
- When they are familiar with the objects and dice, suggest that they take it in turns to toss the dice and say the letter that lands face up. Children choose an object that has the same initial sound as the letter, and put it on the plate labelled with that letter. They keep tossing the dice and choosing objects until one of the plates has five objects on, and that letter is the winner.
- Introduce the doll and suggest the children teach the soft toy how to play the game.
- Play another game with different sets of objects and letters.

What you could say:

- Encourage children to make decisions by asking questions such as: 'How can we decide who will roll the dice first?'
- Help children not only to answer questions but also to ask them: 'Has anyone spotted what's the same about these two objects?'
- Model tossing the dice, choosing an object and deciding what plate it should go on: 'I wonder if I should put the dinosaur on the 'D' plate?'
- Verbalise any issues that are developing with children's sound/letter identification.

Another great idea:

- Play a different game using six circles numbered one to six, 36 small assorted objects, a soft teddy, and a one to six dice.
- Put six of the objects on each circle. The first player tosses the dice, says the number, puts the teddy on that number circle and then takes one of the objects from that circle.
- The second player throws the dice, says the number, moves the teddy on to that number circle and takes one of the objects from that circle.
- The game ends when the teddy is moved onto a number circle and there are no objects to take.
- Everyone counts how many objects they have collected, and then has the opportunity to swap any objects they want to change with other players. They may use their grouping skills here, for example if they have two marbles and one paperclip they may wish to swap the paperclip for a marble. This could turn into a new game!

Looking for a number

This activity is helpful for children who are having issues with recognising particular numerals, and is a good start to assembling numbers in order.

Focus:
Recognising numerals, positional language and being systematic.

What you could provide:

▶ A long piece of trellis, arranged horizontally
▶ A selection of different types of numerals such as plastic, wooden and foam
▶ Lots of number cards, some handwritten and some printed
▶ Pegs
▶ Torches
▶ A number line
▶ A sand timer
▶ Ribbon and paperclips

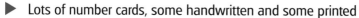

I will need

What you could do:

▶ Help the children peg the numerals and number cards in a random order along the trellis.

▶ Close the blinds or turn off the lights, and shine a torch to highlight a particular number.

▶ Next, shine the torch on the numbers that come between five and nine. Suggest children use the number line to check how many numbers there are between five and nine.

▶ Use the timer to see if anyone can find and un-peg the numbers one to ten before the sand runs out!

▶ Choose a number and then link all those cards with that number by fixing a paper clip on the cards and threading with ribbon.

What you could say:

▶ Make suggestions such as 'Who thinks they could shine the torchlight on the number that is one more than eight?'

▶ Shine the torch on a number and make comments such as 'Is that the number that comes before three?' and 'Oh look, is that a number four?'

▶ Ask questions such as: 'Has anyone seen a number ten on the trellis?'

▶ Help children review the activity by asking: 'So how many number fives have we been able to link on the trellis?'

Another great idea:

▶ Take the numerals into the outdoor area and make a number tree by setting a large branch into a bucket of earth and fixing the numerals on the tree. You could hang all the same numerals and make a 'number six' tree, or make a 'teen' tree by hanging up numbers 13 to 19.

▶ Play 'hide and seek the number' by hiding some numerals in part of the outdoor area and challenging the children to find as many number cards as they can before the sand timer runs out. Find the total number of points scored by each child by adding up the numbers – the highest score wins!

Section 2: Shape, space and measures

Waterfalls

Any play experience where children pour water down pipes and guttering is bound to be successful! In addition, this activity offers practitioners the opportunity to encourage the play to be more mathematical, and to develop children's problem solving techniques.

Focus:

Using the language of shape, speed, angle and length, and talking a problem through, suggesting solutions.

What you could provide:

I will need

▶ An assortment of different lengths and widths of plastic guttering, drainpipes and connectors from a local DIY store

▶ Plastic bucket and a selection of plastic jugs, empty milk containers, plastic tubes and funnels

- Small, light plastic balls that float, such as ping-pong balls
- A mop and bucket so children can clear up water spills

What you could do:

- Build on the children's experiences of water play and floating and sinking. Introduce the guttering and compare different pieces, encouraging children to use words to describe the width and length of it.
- Help children to lean the guttering or pipes against the water tray and into the bucket, and suggest they pour water down them.
- Rehearse pouring the water down the guttering or pipes and investigate how to make it flow quickly or slowly.
- Encourage children to take responsibility for developing the idea of changing the speed of the water by leaning the gutter at different angles and by using different lengths of pipe.
- Add floating objects such as ping-pong balls, and observe how they move along the guttering.

What you could say:

- Try not to intervene too quickly when children hesitate in their explanation of what happened, and instead try nodding and smiling and acting as a listener because this will often get the discussion started again.
- Ask questions such as 'What can you say about the speed that the water flowed down the gutter?' and 'Have you any ideas on how we can make the water flow more slowly along the gutter?'
- Introduce words such as 'trickle', 'drip', 'splash', 'flow', 'fast', 'slow', 'angle' and 'speed'. Make sure the new vocabulary is placed in a meaningful context for the children.
- Observe what the children do and say and use this information to extend the activity. Suggest challenges that are appropriate to the children's needs.

Another great idea:

- Connect a hose to an outside tap and use the water to make patterns and shapes on the ground. Try 'drawing' a spiral or zig-zag lines. Add a showerhead to the end of the hose and make sprinkle designs using large arm movements.

Wind-up toys

Collect a selection of wind-up toys to introduce. Use the language of shape, space, time and speed as well as developing the children's skills of mathematical reasoning.

Focus:

Shape and space, positional language and describing results.

What you could provide:

▶ A selection of wind-up clockwork toys and automatic cars
▶ Paint and brushes, large pieces of paper
▶ Timers

What you could do:

- ▶ Play with the wind-up toys alongside the children, observing how the toys move – whether in straight lines, circling movements or apparently randomly.

- ▶ Demonstrate for children who are unsure how to wind the toys up and set them moving.

- ▶ Suggest children paint the feet of the wind up toys or dip the wheels of the cars in paint (or water), and then put them on large sheets of paper to record the line of movement.

- ▶ Note which children compare the difference between the movements the toys make.

- ▶ Suggest the children pretend to be clockwork toys. Each child should ask a friend to 'wind them up' and then move mechanically either in circles or straight lines.

What you could say:

- ▶ Make comments on the movement patterns that the wind-up toys make, such as: 'Oh, look! Mine keeps going round and round in circles!'

- ▶ Think aloud by making comments such as: 'I wonder if there any other toys that make the same movement lines as that one?'

- ▶ Challenge children to extend their thinking and mathematical language by asking questions such as: 'Is there another way to describe how the toy moves?'

- ▶ Talk about how they could find out which toy runs for the longest time.

Another great idea:

- ▶ Provide pieces of paper and foil food trays. Each piece of paper should fit across the bottom of a tray. Paint a marble in thick paint and then, while the paint is still wet, roll the marble round the tray. Discuss whether the marble made circular movements or moved in straight lines.

- ▶ Construct two marble runs and time how long it takes for the marble to reach the end. Compare and decide which run took the most time for the marble to emerge.

- ▶ Cover the floor in old sheets or large pieces of paper. Put down a tray of paint for children to walk through barefoot and to make movement lines similar to the wind-up toys.

Camping

Constructing camps and dens outdoors is a good way to give children the opportunity to be involved in a lot of problem solving experiences and construction skills learning.

Focus:

Using the language of position, shape and space; explaining and finding solutions to practical problems.

What you could provide:

▶ Materials to construct a tent or den, such as sheets, curtains and poles

▶ Rucksacks, water bottles

▶ Binoculars and bird books

▶ Compasses and maps

▶ An oven shelf and bricks to build a campfire or barbecue

▶ Buckets, bowls and water for washing up

What you could do:

▶ Encourage the children to explore the resources and decide which materials they need to build a camp or den. Offer extra resources as they are needed.

▶ Talk with the children about the best place to put up a tent or make a den, and and where to build a barbecue. Use positional words and phrases during the discussion.

▶ Sit in a circle and sing songs round a real or pretend campfire.

▶ Go on a scavenger hunt collecting stones, twigs and leaves, then go back to the campsite and sort the items into groups. Support children in identifying their objects.

▶ Lay a crumb trail round the outdoor area for children to follow. Make sure that there is something exciting at the end of the trail! It could be a large toy crocodile sitting in a puddle, or a 'bear' in a cave. You can also make a trail with twigs arranged as arrows. When children are following a trail it gives you the opportunity to use vocabulary such as 'straight', 'turn', 'curve' and 'zig-zag'.

What you could say:

▶ Encourage children to try different solutions to practical problems and use a running commentary on what is happening, without necessarily providing the solution to the problem.

▶ Support children in finding a solution by making statements such as: 'Hmm, the arrow is pointing to the right...'

▶ Look for opportunities to develop children's mathematical reasoning skills by making comments such as: 'I wonder why Thomas chose that box to go on the top of his den?'.

Another great idea:

▶ Create a campsite for small world play. Offer a range of materials for tent-making.

▶ Build a house for a hedgehog using logs and damp leaves.

▶ Make trail mix for eating at snack time!

▶ Put up a very large tent so that everyone can sit in it and tell stories and sing songs.

Keep-fit centre

Suggest children set up a 'keep-fit centre' where they can explore and develop different skills and rehearse those skills in a new context.

Focus:

Explaining and identifying patterns, using the language of measurement to describe size, and describing solutions to practical problems.

What you could provide:

▶ Skipping ropes, hoops

▶ Exercise mats, stopwatches, whistles, sand timers, mirror

▶ Head bands, wrist bands, towels

▶ Mini trampoline, balance beam, large wooden bricks or benches to use for step-ups

▶ CD player

What you could do:

▶ Suggest putting together a floor plan of where the equipment could go. Scaled down cut-outs which can be arranged and rearranged on paper will make this an easier task for the children.

▶ Involve children in putting out the equipment; work as a group to see if everything will fit into the space.

▶ Discuss warming up and the importance of slowly stretching your arms and legs before you start exercising.

▶ Help children to put together their own schedules at the 'keep-fit centre', such as: Do three hops, then four starjumps and five step-ups.

▶ Provide charts for children to fill in as they progress round the 'keep-fit centre'. Support them in their record-making.

▶ Encourage children to make a set of challenge cards or posters on how to keep fit.

▶ Work out alongside the children and demonstrate a skill such as hopping or skipping.

▶ Value what each child achieves and encourage them to compare and improve on their own skills.

What you could say:

▶ Ask questions such as 'Can you do more hops than you did last time?'

▶ Comment on the how many bean bags you can you balance on your head.

▶ Discuss with children which skills they find difficult and which they find easier.

▶ Remind children about warming up and warming down.

▶ Suggest children estimate how many jumps or hops they think they will be able to do before they start the exercise.

Another great idea:

▶ Provide a selection of equipment and ask children to help set up a training circuit in the outdoor area. Include tunnels, hoops and skipping ropes. Suggest that children find the fastest route around the circuit!

Here is the news

Talking through the happenings of the day is a particular delight for both adults and for young children. By reflecting on what they have done, children can build on some great learning experiences. Having a news board that children both organise and contribute to will give them the opportunity to look back on what has occurred that day or during that week.

Focus:

Measuring, shape, positional language, reasoning and predicting

What you could provide:

▶ A large board (such as a pin board or classroom display board), covered in paper

▶ Blu-Tack and sticky tape

▶ Photographs and paintings

▶ A computer and printer to generate headings

What you could do:

▶ Put out on a table the photographs, drawings and notices that the children decide they want to include on the news board. Go along with the children's ideas and reasoning as far as possible, but this doesn't mean you can't offer your suggestions that could develop and build on their ideas.

▶ Look at newspaper front pages, including these from local papers. Draw children's attention to the date and discuss why newspapers would need a date.

▶ Show the name of the paper and vote on the title of what your news board could be called.

▶ Suggest that the children come up with a list of things that need to be done; you could scribe this for them.

▶ Decide how large the news board could be and where the best place is for it. Walk around the setting with the children and comment together on the suitability of each proposed site.

▶ Collect and choose together what photos and drawings should be on the board. Children should dictate what text they want – it could be typed and printed from the computer, or you may prefer for them to write it themselves.

▶ Note the children who are working together and showing a sense of satisfaction with their own achievements.

What you could say:

▶ Make comments about fitting the chosen pieces of news and photos on the board: 'Do you think the board is big enough to fit on all the photos you've chosen? Do we need more space?'

▶ Support their developing systematic skills by referring to their to-do list: 'Can anyone suggest what we could do next?'

▶ Ask questions such as: 'How did you all decide which photo to put in that space on the news board?'

Another great idea:

▶ Support children in making and displaying a large 'Forthcoming Events' calendar. Include birthdays, outings and visitors expected.

Foil fun

Introduce rolls of aluminum foil into the creative area and children will quickly become very absorbed and adept in making models and sculptures! Use their interest as a springboard for some maths problem-solving.

Focus:

Using the language of 3D shape, describing what they see and suggesting a practical solution to a problem.

What you could provide:

► Rolls of aluminum foil
► Various pieces of foil, pre-cut in different lengths, sizes and shapes
► Crayons, scissors, paint rollers, paints and brushes
► Masking tape, hole punches, paperclips, wool and string
► Plastic shapes, stones

I will need

What you could do:

▶ Draw children's attention to how the look and shape of the foil changes as they handle it.

▶ Demonstrate folding the edges over to join pieces of foil together, and rolling foil to make lengths that can be bent into skeletal shapes.

▶ Encourage the children to discover different qualities of the foil; for instance, how it will hold the shape of any object it is wrapped around even when the object is (carefully) removed.

▶ Play a game of 'guess what has been inside my foil parcel?' by comparing the shape it leaves with a selection of different objects. Ask the children to explain how they knew it was, for instance, the mug that had been wrapped in the foil.

▶ Share children's expertise at using the foil by asking how they made a particular model, and wonder aloud how you could create something similar.

▶ Note children who are explaining to others and giving reasons for what they are doing and suggesting solutions.

▶ Use a paint roller to make impressions of an object wrapped in the foil and then ask for suggestions as to what the object could be.

What you could say:

▶ Make comments using words such as 'twisting', 'scrunching', 'crumpling' and 'smoothing' to describe how children are handling the foil

▶ When you are working with the foil say what you are doing and model asking for support: 'I'm going to make a design on my piece of foil, can anybody help me?'

▶ Use a shape name when appropriate and connect the shape to the spoken word by touching it or drawing the outline in the air with your fingers.

▶ Ask questions such as: 'Has anyone got a good idea how Jake can make the arms on his model stay on?'

Another great idea:

▶ Use florists' wire to make more sculptures.

▶ Have a sculpture exhibition showing the foil sculptures.

▶ Make a big sculpture all together using recycled materials and then spray it silver.

Bread making

Transfer children's fascination and skills in working with malleable materials, such as play dough, to making and eating some real bread! Solve some practical problems in this activity with groups of six.

Focus:
Weight, capacity, and choosing and using own methods to find a solution.

What you could provide:

The following ingredients make about 12 small bread rolls:

▶ 750g strong white flour
▶ 7g sachet of dried yeast
▶ One teaspoon of salt
▶ Two teaspoons of sunflower oil
▶ 450ml warm water
▶ A large bowl, wooden spoon, cling-film, baking tray, timer, scales

What you could do:

- ▶ Support the children as they weigh the ingredients, tip them into a large bowl and mix together. Take it in turns to knead the dough.

- ▶ Divide the dough into six pieces and share amongst the children (work in six groups). Groups should continue to knead their own piece of dough and divide it in half to make two rolls.

- ▶ Encourage the children to work out how many bread rolls there will be if each group makes two rolls each.

- ▶ Put the rolls on a baking sheet, cover with cling film and put in a warm place for one hour to rise. Cook in the oven at 220°C/Gas mark 7 for 10 - 12 minutes.

- ▶ Support the children in making a simple strip cartoon or photo montage showing the sequence of making bread rolls.

What you could say:

- ▶ Discuss the feel of the dough using descriptive words such as 'squishy' and 'squelchy'! Encourage the children to invent their own descriptive words.

- ▶ Talk about the order to do things in, asking what do you need to do next.

- ▶ Discuss with the group how they can share the dough out fairly.

- ▶ Make suggestions such as: 'Do you think we should weigh that again, just to make sure?'

- ▶ Ask questions such as: 'How could we use the timer to work out when the dough is ready to cook?'

Another great idea:

- ▶ On a cold day, invite the children to make a warm chocolate drink for everyone.

- ▶ Use instant drinking chocolate and milk and heat in a microwave oven.

- ▶ Decide together how long to heat the milk and take it in turns to set the minutes on the microwave oven timer.

From A to B

Children rarely have the opportunity to investigate objects that are really heavy. Sometimes they have two objects and are asked the question 'which one is heaviest?', when really both objects are light. This experience gives children the chance to explore genuinely heavy things in a safe environment.

Focus:

Measures – weight; co-operating and finding new ways to do things.

What you could provide:

I will need

▶ A building site in the outdoor area – include hard hats, builders' buckets, small buckets, shovels, spades, water, sand, pebbles, gravel, guttering, building blocks, huge cardboard boxes and fabric, all on a tarpaulin

▶ Some distance away, builders' buckets filled with damp sand and large gravel.

▶ Bucket balances and bathroom scales

▶ A wheelbarrow or play truck

What you could do:

▶ Observe the children as they explore the building site and the buckets full of sand and gravel.

▶ Listen to the discussions the children have about moving the sand and the gravel to the building site. What language do they use?

▶ Note the strategies they use when they can't lift the large buckets – who empties some of the sand into smaller buckets? Who works together collaboratively to move the full bucket? Does anyone introduce another strategy, e.g. finding a wheelbarrow or pull-along truck?

▶ Where appropriate, join in the children's play as a co-player.

What you could say:

▶ Act in role as a customer or new builder: 'How can I get all this sand into my car?' 'How much sand and gravel do we need to make the cement?'

▶ Model the language of weight: 'heavy', 'heavier than', 'heaviest', 'light', 'lighter than', 'lightest'; 'about the same weight as'; 'as heavy as'; 'balance'; 'weigh'.

▶ Talk to the children about what they are doing and why – lifting, carrying, moving, dragging, pulling, digging...

Another great idea:

▶ In your preparation, wrap up pairs of identically sized boxes – some small and some large. Ensure that each matching-sized pair of boxes includes one that is noticeably heavier than the other.

▶ Spread out all the boxes. Children take it in turns to touch two boxes that are the same size. The child who touches the boxes then chooses just one of the pair to pick up.

▶ The child predicts whether the second box will be 'lighter than' or 'heavier than' the first box, and lifts to confirm.

▶ When all the boxes have been tried, work together to order all the boxes by weight.

▶ Look at the boxes – not all the big boxes are heavy, and not all the small boxes are light!

Terrific ties

This is a great activity to start children thinking about non-standard measures and developing their problem-solving strategies together.

Focus:

Measures – length; having their own ideas and checking how well their activities are going.

What you could provide:

▶ An interesting collection of neck ties with different patterns, colours and textures

▶ If you have access to shorter school ties, include those too (optional)

▶ A wicker basket

What you could do:

▶ Introduce the wicker basket full of assorted ties to a small group of children. Try to include some children who have shown an interest in length and measuring things.

▶ Explore the ties together and talk about them – what is the same, and what is different?

- ▶ When the children begin to talk about length, ask appropriate questions (see 'What you could say' section).
- ▶ Try to predict how many ties it is from one point to another, e.g. from the door to the window.
- ▶ Now try it out – making sure this is 'fair'.
- ▶ When you have used the ties to measure one distance, support children as they use their problem-solving skills to predict other distances and confirm their hypothesis.
- ▶ Challenge the children to measure something that is not in a straight line – a circular playground marking, or a chalked route.
- ▶ Note the strategies that children use.

What you could say:

- ▶ Talk to the children about what they are doing and why.
- ▶ Make comments about what you can see: 'Mm – that tie isn't quite straight!'
- ▶ Make comments about what is happening: 'Oh, I see you are leaving a gap between the ties.'
- ▶ Ask questions: 'Do you think it is fair if the ties overlap?'; 'Oh no, we are running out of ties – what are we going to do?'
- ▶ Provide scaffolding for children's own questions and support them as they answer each other's questions.
- ▶ Make links with home experiences: 'I used to help my son tie his school tie – it was very tricky.'
- ▶ Model vocabulary use: 'long', 'measure', 'distance'.

Another great idea:

- ▶ Introduce the storybook '"Pardon?" Said the Giraffe', by Colin West, which is about a very tall giraffe with a very long neck!
- ▶ Talk to the children about 'tall' and 'long'.
- ▶ Provide two baskets and support children as they make collections of 'tall' items and 'long' items.
- ▶ Model the use of comparative vocabulary: 'tall', 'taller than', 'tallest,' and 'long', 'longer than' and 'longest'.

Build a box

All children love hiding and playing inside boxes – they can become cars, castles or caves! This experience gives children opportunities to reconstruct flattened boxes and explore the properties of hollow 3D shapes.

Focus:

3D shape names and properties; positional language; playing with what they know and testing their ideas.

What you could provide:

▶ Several huge, assorted cuboid boxes, carefully flattened so that they can be reconstructed

▶ Masking tape and scissors

▶ Picnic rugs

▶ Photos of local buildings

What you could do:

▶ Lay the flattened boxes on the picnic rugs outdoors.
▶ Observe the children as they explore the flattened cardboard boxes.
▶ Encourage the children to work together collaboratively to construct the boxes and fix them using the masking tape.
▶ If children get stuck, suggest a range of strategies, including reviewing what they have already done and achieved.
▶ When the children have remade the boxes, model the use of positional language such as 'in', 'on' and 'next to'.
▶ Introduce the rhyme 'Jack in a Box, Jack in a Box, open the lid and out s/he pops!'
▶ Note how children make decisions about how to approach the task, negotiate and reach their goal.

What you could say:

▶ Introduce and model the use of the language of 3D shape: 'hollow shape', 'cube', 'cuboid', 'edge', 'corner', 'face', 'same', 'different'.
▶ Discuss what sort of shape the flat cardboard could be made into.
▶ Support children's own conversations about what they are doing and why.
▶ Talk to children about what they are doing and why.
▶ Model the use of ordinal numbers: 'What did you do first? And second?'
▶ Help children to express their mathematical thinking as they problem-solve when re-constructing the box: 'What do you think you need to do next?'; 'How could you fix that edge?'
▶ Support children as they describe and discuss shapes and patterns and use simple words to describe the position of objects.
▶ Talk to the children about other cubes and cuboids in the setting, e.g. construction blocks.

Another great idea:

▶ Provide a selection of hollow cartons in different sizes and shapes.
▶ Add assorted fixing materials including glue sticks and masking tape.
▶ Make sure paint, brushes and collage materials are available.
▶ Present everything in the creative workshop area, ensuring images of local buildings are displayed at children's eye-level for inspiration.
▶ Support children as they pile up boxes or fix them together.
▶ Talk about the shapes of the boxes and their properties.

All wrapped up!

This challenge gives children opportunities to explore 3D shapes in fun and exciting way. The activity can be introduced as part of a 'Birthdays' theme or as a Christmas challenge.

Focus:

3D shape names and properties; planning how to reach a goal and thinking of ideas.

What you could provide:

▶ Assorted small, empty, cuboid cardboard boxes
▶ Two rolls of gift-wrapping paper
▶ Sticky tape
▶ Rolls of ribbon (optional)

What you could do:

▶ Introduce the activity to two small groups of children. The challenge is for children to wrap as many 'presents' as they can using just one roll of gift-wrapping paper.
▶ Support the children in predicting how many parcels they can wrap. How many small parcels? How many large parcels?

- ▶ Observe which children use a 'trial and error' approach, and which children try to predict the amount of paper needed to wrap an individual box.
- ▶ Note how children choose the boxes they will wrap and how they explain their selection.
- ▶ As children are cutting the paper, encourage them to discuss the best way to predict how much is needed.
- ▶ When all the parcels are wrapped, make two piles with the children and compare. Which group has wrapped the most parcels? Why?
- ▶ Now give the children opportunity to use ribbon to wrap around the parcels – how do they predict how much is needed?
- ▶ Note children who persist with the activity when challenges occur and those who use alternative approaches.

What you could say:

- ▶ Clarify the challenge with the children: this is not about time and how quickly the parcels can be wrapped, it is about wrapping as many as possible with the amount of paper they have.
- ▶ Ask questions such as: 'How much paper do you need to wrap that parcel?'; 'Is that enough paper?'; 'Is that too much paper?'
- ▶ Make connections with children's home experiences – when have they wrapped parcels before?
- ▶ Make comments about what you are doing: 'I wonder if there is enough paper left to wrap two more parcels?'; 'I wonder if it makes a difference which way we wrap the parcel?'
- ▶ Provide scaffolding for children's own questions and support them as they answer each other's questions.

Another great idea:

- ▶ Make collections of pairs of identical objects, including regular and irregular 3D shapes. Wrap one of each pair in aluminum foil.
- ▶ Take it in turns to look at the unwrapped objects together and identify its wrapped 'twin'. Unwrap the package to confirm.
- ▶ Ask children to explain their choices and note the mathematical language they use.

Sticks and stones

Young children need time and space to handle lots of different types of shapes and begin to appreciate their varying properties. It is important that this includes not just regular shapes but irregular ones as well. Exploring natural objects is a great way to begin.

Focus:
Patterns; symmetry; making links; finding out and exploring.

What you could provide:

▶ Small wooden and bamboo trays

▶ Wicker baskets

▶ Twigs, shells, pebbles, gravel, leaves, flowers, fir cones, conkers and other natural materials

▶ Small wooden circles – embroidery hoops are ideal

▶ A digital camera

What you could do:

▶ Present the materials in wicker baskets and on wooden trays.

▶ Observe, wait and listen to see what the children do with the materials – do they sort them or do they begin to make patterns and designs?

▶ Note how children sort the objects using different criteria.

▶ Note the problems children identify and the strategies they use to solve them – what happens if they are using leaves to make a circle in the hoop and they run out?

▶ Follow a pattern a child is making, using another hoop – copy and extend the pattern.

▶ Support children as they make a digital image of their design.

▶ Print out the photo of the design with the child and act as a scribe to record what they say about their design, noting mathematical language used.

What you could say:

▶ Talk to children about things that are the same and things that are different.

▶ Model the use of the language of flat shapes: 'circle', 'triangle', 'square', 'rectangle', 'side', 'corner', 'straight', 'round'.

▶ Ask children about what they are doing and why. Talk to them about their designs or repeating patterns.

▶ Support children as they describe their own patterns, or model talking about them, adding descriptive vocabulary.

▶ Use positional language as you create your own design, e.g. 'next to', 'over', 'under', 'position', 'between'.

Another great idea:

▶ Make a collection of natural objects and opaque materials, e.g. skeleton leaves, netting, coloured acetate, gauze.

▶ Provide a light box or overhead projector and screen.

▶ Support children as they use the irregular objects to make designs and/or repeating patterns on the light box, or to project on a screen or blank wall.

Slithering snakes

Many children love to be just a little bit frightened, in a safe, secure environment, and this snake-related activity gives them the perfect opportunity! The open-ended play experience gives children the time and space to find out more about length.

Focus:

Measures – length; making decisions about how to approach a task.

What you could provide:

I will need

▶ Cooked play dough in two snake-like colours (perhaps green and yellow)
▶ Dried pulses for eyes
▶ Small baskets and boxes
▶ Laminated images of snakes

What you could do:

▶ Present the play dough in an attractive manner – small balls of dough and a few snakes of different lengths.

▶ Make a snake in two colours.

▶ Support the children as they explore the materials – some making snakes (or worms), others making balls or simply exploring flattening the dough.

▶ Observe children and follow their play themes, extending where appropriate.

▶ Observe the problems children identify and how they solve them, e.g. what strategies do they use when they want to make a snake longer? Do they roll it thinner, or add more dough? What strategies do they use to make a two-coloured snake?

▶ Offer possible strategies, e.g. if a child wants to make a very long snake, discuss alternatives such as joining several snakes together.

What you could say:

▶ Talk to the children about what they are doing and why.

▶ Make comments about what is happening: 'Wow, you are making that green snake a lot longer than the yellow one.'

▶ Ask questions: 'I wonder how we could make a snake as long as the table?'

▶ Make links with earlier experiences, e.g. 'Do you remember when the 'Animal Man' brought the real snake to the nursery?'

▶ Make comments about what you are doing: 'I wonder how I could make a stripey snake?'

▶ Model the use of the language of length: 'long', 'longer than', 'longest'.

▶ Introduce the language of standard measures – focus on centimetres.

Another great idea:

▶ Create a snake habitat in a black tray – perhaps by growing grass from seed with the children.

▶ Add boulders, pebbles, plants, bark chips, logs, branches and other natural materials for snakes to hide under, or bask on.

▶ Provide assorted plastic, fabric, rubber and wooden snakes for children to explore.

▶ Add photographs and books about snakes.

▶ Support children as they explore the length of the snakes.

In a minute

'In a minute' is a phrase children often hear, but it often used to mean something else entirely – 'later', 'in an hour' or sometimes 'no, never'! This challenge gives children opportunities to explore time, initially with an adult.

Focus:

Measures – time; keeping on trying and making predictions.

What you could provide:

▶ A one-minute and a two-minute sand timer
▶ Tweezers or tongs
▶ Small animals in a small basket and a wooden tray

What you could do:

▶ Introduce a challenge to the children: 'Jump up and down for one minute and then sit down'. See how many children are still jumping when the one-minute sand timer runs out.

▶ Let the children explore the timers.

▶ Now set children another challenge: 'How many animals can you move from the basket to the tray before the one-minute sand timer runs out?'

▶ Count the objects with the children and ask the question: 'If you moved three animals in one minute, how many can you move in two minutes?' Give children the opportunity to try it and see.

▶ Note how many children predict double the number of objects in two minutes.

▶ Encourage the children to set their own challenges and use the timers independently.

▶ Revisit or introduce the storybook 'Five Minutes' Peace', by Jill Murphy.

What you could say:

▶ Introduce the idea of 'double' and, where appropriate, count in twos.

▶ Talk to the children generally about 'time', including 'a short time' and 'a long time' – is a minute a short time?

▶ Discuss other ways of measuring one minute – 'how could we do that?'

▶ Remind children about other times they may have used timers, e.g. baking.

▶ Ask the children what else they think they could do in just one minute – what about two minutes, or five minutes?

Another great idea:

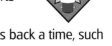

▶ Introduce or revisit the game 'What's the time Mr Wolf?'

▶ All children start at one side of the outdoor area; the adult starts as the Wolf.

▶ Everyone chants 'What's the time Mr Wolf?', and the Wolf calls back a time, such as 'two o'clock' or 'four o'clock'.

▶ The children take the correct number of steps to match the time – e.g. two or four steps – towards the Wolf.

▶ This goes on until the Wolf's answer is 'Dinner Time!', when all the children have to run for 'home' before the Wolf catches them.

Further reading and resources

Andrews, A. and Paul Trafton, P (2002)
'Little Kids – Powerful Problem Solvers': Maths Stories from a Kindergarten Classroom, Heinnemann

Beckley, P. et al (2010)
'Problem Solving, Reasoning and Numeracy', Continuum

Bennett, E. and Weidner, J. (2011)
'Everyday Maths through Everyday Provision: Developing opportunities for mathematics in the early years', Routledge

Bennett, E. and Weidner, J. (2013)
'The Building Blocks of Everyday Maths: Bringing key concepts to life in the Early Years and Key Stage 1', Routledge

Skinner, C. (2005)
'Maths Outdoors', BEAM

Skinner, C. and Stevens, J. (2013)
'Foundations of Mathematics: An Active Approach to Number, Shape and Measures in the Early Years', Featherstone

Smith, S. (2006)
'Early Childhood Mathematics', Pearson

Stevens, J. (2008)
'Maths in Stories', BEAM

Stevens, J. (2009)
'Maths Now! Early Years Foundation Stage', BEAM 2009

Stevens, J. (2013)
'Maths Development Wheel: A guide for parents, carers and practitioners', Early Years and Childcare Publishing Partnership, KMMD Publishing

www.nrich.maths.org

The Little Books Club

There is always something in Little Books to help and inspire you. Packed full of lovely ideas, Little Books meet the need for exciting and practical activities that are fun to do, address the Early Learning Goals and can be followed in most settings. Everyone is a winner!

We publish 5 new Little Books a year. Little Books Club members receive each of these 5 books as soon as they are published for a reduced price. The subscription cost is £29.99 – a one off payment that buys the 5 new books for £4.99 instead of £8.99 each.

In addition to this, Little Books Club Members receive:
· Free postage and packing on anything ordered from the Featherstone catalogue
· A 15% discount voucher upon joining which can be used to buy any number of books from the Featherstone catalogue
· Members price of £4.99 on any additional Little Book purchased
· A regular, free newsletter dealing with club news, special offers and aspects of Early Years curriculum and practice
· All new Little Books on approval - return in good condition within 30 days and we'll refund the cost to your club account

Call 020 7758 0200 or email: littlebooks@bloomsbury.com for an enrolment pack. Or download an application form from our website:
www.bloomsbury.com

The **Little Books** series consists of:

50
All through the year
Bags, Boxes & Trays
Big Projects
Bricks & Boxes
Celebrations
Christmas
Circle Time
Clay and Malleable Materials
Clothes and Fabric
Colour, Shape and Number
Cooking from Stories
Cooking Together
Counting
Dance
Dance Music CD
Dens
Discovery Bottles
Dough
Drama from Stories
Explorations
Fine Motor Skills
Free and Found
Fun on a Shoestring
Games with Sounds
Gross Motor Skills
Growing Things
ICT
Investigations
Junk Music
Kitchen Stuff

Language Fun
Light and Shadow
Listening
Living Things
Look and Listen
Making Books and Cards
Making Poetry
Maps and Plans
Mark Making
Maths Activities
Maths from Stories
Maths Outdoors
Maths Problem Solving
Maths Songs and Games
Messy Play
Minibeast Hotels
Multi-sensory Stories
Music
Nursery Rhymes
Opposites
Outdoor Play
Outside in All Weathers
Painting
Parachute Play
Persona Dolls
Phonics
Playground Games
Prop Boxes for Role Play
Props for Writing
Puppet Making
Puppets in Stories

Resistant Materials
Rhythm and Raps
Role Play
Role Play Windows
Sand and Water
Science through Art
Scissor Skills
Seasons
Sequencing Skills
Sewing and Weaving
Small World Play
Sound Ideas
Special Days
Stories from around the world
Story bags
Storyboards
Storybuilding
Storytelling
Time and Money
Time and Place
Topsy Turvy
Traditional Tales
Treasure Baskets
Treasure Boxes
Tuff Spot Activities
Washing lines
Woodwork
Writing

All available from
www.bloomsbury.com